15 Reproducible Spanish Write-and-Read Books

Instant Patterns for Easy Predictable Books Your Students Help Write!

by Veronica Robillard

SCHOLASTIC
PROFESSIONAL BOOKS

New York ❧ Toronto ❧ London ❧ Auckland ❧ Sydney

Dedication

To Kenneth, Christine, and Kevin, whose support,
patience, and encouragement have clearly been the
basis for my sustenance and personal growth.

Teachers may photocopy the reproducible pages in this book for classroom use. No other
part of this publication may be reproduced in whole or in part, or stored in a retrieval
system, or transmitted in any form or by any means, electronic, mechanical, photocopy,
recording, or otherwise, without written permission of the publisher. For information
regarding permission, write to Scholastic Inc., 555 Broadway, New York, NY 10012.

Cover design by Vincent Ceci and Jaime Lucero

Cover photography by Robert Lorenz

Interior design by Ellen Matlach Hassell
for Boultinghouse & Boultinghouse, Inc.

Cover and interior illustrations by Maxie Chambliss

ISBN 0-439-05176-2

Copyright © 1997 by Veronica Robillard

Contenido

❧ Introduction ❧

Write-and-Read Books are fun to make and are rewarding tools for emerging readers. These books foster interactive learning and promote the unique creativity of each learner while providing authentic instruction in skills and concepts. Using the predictable, patterned stories in the templates, children write and illustrate their own books, which they can then take home and share. Children learn by writing, reading, listening, and speaking. They also learn from the feedback and support of their audience.

At the earliest stages of the process, children experience success and a sense of ownership. They realize that they *can* do the writing and the reading. The process is self-nourishing. As children develop confidence, they are motivated to write more and to read what they have written.

The books are simple to construct and easy to use. I usually make a model of each book and share it with the class as I introduce the concept. (You'll find suggestions for presenting individual books on pages 5–16.)

The children complete the books in keeping with their own literacy development. The amount of direction and instruction depends on children's needs. Preliminary group work on the chalkboard or chart pads is often helpful in supporting their efforts. For early learners, I sometimes dot letters or write them in yellow fine marker as children dictate the words for their stories. For advanced learners, I encourage a more colorful and detailed text. Illustrating the stories provides children with another way to express their ideas and knowledge.

The amount of time and the depth of the lessons for each book vary. I encourage you to extend the concepts and ideas to the degree that time, resources, and student needs allow.

A critical component is to provide children with the opportunity and encouragement to read their books again and again—to themselves, other students, family members, the principal, or other classes. As they share their books in this way, children learn to use cues such as patterns in the text, or high frequency words, or their illustrations to help them to become fluent readers.

Each book includes a "Comments" page on the back cover. This page provides a place for family members or classmates to respond to—and reinforce—the author's efforts with *positive* comments. You'll find a letter to family members on page 17, which you can duplicate and send home, explaining the importance of this feedback in helping children grow as writers and readers.

I suggest considering a predictable pattern in making and sharing the books. I include them as part of my scheduled routine. We make a book in class each week. Children take their books home every Friday and return them on Monday with responses from family members.

In addition to making the 15 books included here, you and your class may want to write your own stories. Use the templates on pages 94–96 for students' original work.

With write-and-read books, children, teachers, and parents all join together to foster literacy growth. I think you'll find the experience both rewarding and enjoyable.

Veronica Robillard

Getting Started with Write–and–Read Books

Assembling the Books

1. Copy the pages for books on standard 8½-inch by 11-inch paper, making the pages single-sided.

2. Fold the front cover/ back cover in half along the dashed line, keeping the fold to the left side.

3. Fold the inner pages in half, keeping the fold to the right side.

4. Place the inner pages inside the cover and staple three times along the spine.

Because some students might have difficulty assembling the books, you might want to prepare the books before class. When you reproduce each book, be sure to include an About the Author page (see page 94) for children to fill out and insert into their books.

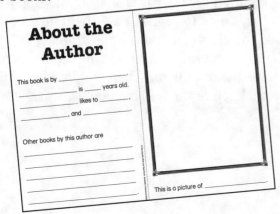

A Rainbow of Colors

SKILLS: Children review basic color names and identify items in these colors.

◎ Strategies for Starting

Talk about the colors that children are wearing. Ask: *Who is wearing something red? something yellow? What color is Nora wearing?* Note similarities in the colors of shirts, pants, or skirts. Invite children to name their favorite colors. Then discuss rainbows. Have children ever seen one? Where? When? What does a rainbow look like? If possible, have photographs from magazines or books on hand to show the class.

◎ Introduce the Book

Display the model book that you made. Read it aloud to the class. Focus on the literary pattern, "I can see a [color name]…Can you?" Discuss the objects that you drew for each color. Encourage children to find other items in the room that are these colors. You may want to list these on a chart paper for children to refer to as they make their own books.

. . . .

Teaching Tip: Using the pattern, "I can see a…," can convince students that they all can read by the end of this lesson. This is a wonderful way to start the school year!

. . . .

◎ Make the Book

Duplicate and pass out pages 20–24 of this book. Help children assemble their *A Rainbow of Colors* books. Explain that students can write and draw whatever they like to represent the color on each page. You may want to brainstorm as a group some common objects for a particular color. For example, on a list for red you might include cherry, strawberry, tomato, fire truck, and heart. Some children may need help writing the names of the objects in their books. Remind children to write their names on the cover.

◎ Share the Book

Invite children to take turns reading their books aloud. Before the reader comes to the last page, have the class guess what that child's favorite color is. Send the books home along with the letter on page 17.

◎ Beyond the Book

Make a class graph of favorite colors.

What Will I Wear?

SKILLS: Children identify items of clothing and review color names. Children recognize the relationship between print and illustrations.

◎ Strategies for Starting

Talk about the various items of clothing that children are wearing. Write the clothing names on the chalkboard as they are mentioned. As each item is named, ask children what color or colors it is. Expand the discussion and ask children how they decide what to wear each day. Ask: *Does someone help you choose? Does the weather influence you?*

How? Do you think about your activities for the day? Why? What other factors help you decide what to wear?

◎ Introduce the Book

Display the model that you have made. As you read it aloud, emphasize the sentence patterns, "Here are my…" or "Here is my…" Help children understand that literary patterns can be helpful when reading a story. Discuss the colors that you used to describe each item. ("Here is my hat. It is red.") Ask children to name other items of clothing in the room that are the same colors.

◎ Make the Book

Duplicate and pass out pages 25–28 of this book. Help children assemble their books.

Discuss the relationship of pictures to print. Explain that pictures can be valuable clues to the words. As an example, compare a picture book without words and a picture book with simple text and rich illustrations. Then point out that children must make the pictures in their *What Will I Wear?* book relate to the words. For example, if a page mentions a hat, children must draw a hat. If they have written that the hat is red, they should draw a red hat. Or, if they draw a red hat, they must write the word *red* to complete the sentence. You may want to list color words on the chalkboard for children to use in their books.

When children get to page 6 of their books, point out that in addition to the items of clothing they have already illustrated on previous pages, they should show one or two other items.

◎ Share the Book

Invite children to take turns sharing their books. When they come to page 6, have them hold up the book so the class can find the "new" items.

Send the books home and invite family members to respond to them. When children bring the books back, place them in a reading corner.

Beyond the Book

Hold a "fashion show." Ask children to identify the clothing they are wearing and to use color words and other adjectives to describe it.

Teaching Tip: You can also use *What Will I Wear?* to teach size words or other kinds of adjectives. Instead of colors, have children describe the clothing with words such as *large, baggy, tight* or *pretty, dirty, new.*

My Friend

SKILLS: Children recognize the importance of friendship and identify things they do with friends.

Strategies for Starting

Have children hypothesize about friends and friendships by asking questions such as: *How do you know when someone is your friend? What do you like to do with your friends? What are the things you like best about your friends? Why are friends important? How can they help you? How do you think you should treat friends? Why? How do you want friends to treat you?* You may also want to have available for discussion several picture books about friendships.

Introduce the Book

Show children the model book that you made. Before reading the story aloud, you may want to point out that although the book is about just one friend, there are other people you like to do things with, too.

Make the Book

Duplicate and pass out pages 29–32 of this book. Help children assemble their books. Ask children to choose a friend to feature in their book. If children have trouble choosing one friend, suggest that they can make additional books at a later time. Some children might even want to write about an imaginary friend. You may need to work with individual students to complete the sentences in their books. You can also write possible words for each sentence on the chalkboard for students to copy. For example: "We always [play, read, talk, eat] together." Be sure that children illustrate the activities that they write about.

Share the Book

Invite children to share their completed books with friends.

Send the books home for children to read with family members. When the books are returned to class with comments, use them as part of a bulletin board display on the theme of friendship.

Beyond the Book

Use the books to generate a class graph of favorite activities students do with their friends. Keep a copy for the classroom and send other copies home.

My Pet

SKILLS: Children learn about animals that are pets.

Strategies for Starting

Have a discussion with children about pets that they have, once had, or would like to have. Make a list of popular pets including dogs, cats, rabbits, fish, gerbils, hamsters, and birds. Talk about how

these animals are special and why people enjoy having them as pets. Encourage children to share stories and information about their own pets. With the class, develop a list of responsibilities people have in caring for their pets. Have available a selection of books on pets and pet care for children to use.

☺ Introduce the Book

Share the model book that you made. If children don't have a pet, invite them to choose an imaginary one. Mention that not everyone has a pet; some people don't want them, can't take care of them, or don't live in places where pets are allowed.

☺ Make the Book

Duplicate and pass out pages 33–35 of this book. Help children assemble their *My Pet* books. As children choose a pet to feature, write the name of that animal on a chart or on the chalkboard. Next to each kind of animal, have children list places that the animal would sleep and food that it would eat. If children are unsure of an animal's habits, help them use the books you collected to find out more. After children have completed the sentences, allow time for them to illustrate their books.

☺ Share the Book

Invite children to share their books with the class. Ask the listeners to respond with positive comments. You may want to give examples beforehand. For example: "I like the name you chose for your pet. Your illustrations tell me a lot about your pet. I can see that you care about this animal."

Send the books home for children to read to family members.

☺ Beyond the Book

Hold a class pet show. Have each child draw a large portrait of the pet he or she featured in the book. On the day of the show, have children hold up their pictures as you lead them in a parade around the room. Then invite different pet "owners" to tell the class about their pets. Encourage students to tell what their pet eats, what other care it needs, and how they play with it.

Does a Pig Wear a Wig?

SKILLS: Children use rhyming words and identify sentence patterns.

☺ Strategies for Starting

Ask children to give examples of words that rhyme. Use their suggestions to create a rhyming chart on the chalkboard.

☺ Introduce the Book

Display the model book that you made. Ask children to listen for the rhymes as you read the book aloud. Draw children's attention to the pattern, "Does a [pig] wear a...?"

☺ Make the Book

Duplicate and pass out pages 36–40 of this book. Have children assemble their books and color the pictures. Point out that in this book children will complete the question on each page with a rhyming word. Children should use the illustration on each page as a clue to what the rhyming word will be. You may want to write all the rhyming words—*wig, shoe, coat, mitten, blouse, ribbon, tie, hat*—on the chalkboard for children to copy.

☺ Share the Book

Read the book together with the class. After each question, you might have children respond by shouting a patterned response such as, "No! A pig does not wear a wig" or "Yes! My pig wears a wig."

Send the books home for children to share with family members. When children return the books to school, read aloud some of the responses.

◎ Beyond the Book

Extend your lessons in rhyming patterns by giving children similar sentences to complete such as: Does a snail get [mail]? Does a frog sit on a [log]? Can a duck drive a [truck]? Invite children to make up their own rhyming sentences for partners to complete.

. . . .

Teaching Tip: For an extra challenge, encourage children to make up rhyming sentences to create their own version of the book *Does a Pig Wear a Wig?* They can complete their books by illustrating their sentences.

. . . .

My Surprise

SKILLS: Children identify rooms in a home and predict a story ending.

◎ Strategies for Starting

Ask children to name the different rooms in their homes. Use prompts to discuss the function of various rooms by asking: *In what room do you sleep? eat? read? take a bath? In what room do you have a sofa? a bureau? a sink?* Talk about other furnishings found in different rooms, stressing that homes vary according to personal tastes and lifestyles. If a dollhouse is available, you might use it as a prop during this discussion. Then ask: *Have you ever had a nice surprise when you got home? What was it?*

◎ Introduce the Book

Share the first several pages of the book that you completed as a model. Draw children's attention to the pattern, "I went into the [hall]. No one was there." Before reading aloud the ending, ask chil-

dren to speculate on why no one is in any of the rooms. Then have children predict what happens in the backyard. After reading the story ending, ask: *Why is the title of this book* My Surprise?

◎ Make the Book

Duplicate and pass out pages 41–44 of this book. Help children assemble their books and color the pictures. Point out that on the first page all the text is given, but children must complete the text on the subsequent pages. Ask how they know what word to add to page 2. *(by using the picture)* Point out that on page 3, children should trace the words in the second sentence. On page 4, ask: *What words should you write for the second sentence? Why?* Help children recognize the pattern, "No one was there."

◎ Share the Book

Children might work with partners to read their books together. One student reads the first sentence on each page, and the partner reads the second sentence. Children then switch and read the book again.

Send the books home for children to read to family members.

If your class is or will be studying homes or special celebrations in social studies, plan to place the books on a table with other resources about these topics.

◎ Beyond the Book

● Follow up by having children make a diorama or floor plan of their homes.

● Some children might want to make additional books about their own birthday celebrations.

Five Frosty Snowmen

SKILLS: Children recognize and use rhyming words and ordinal numbers. Children identify direct quotations. Children relate weather conditions to seasons.

Strategies for Starting

Give children practice in using ordinal numbers. Have five children line up in a row. Ask a volunteer to point to the first child. Then ask: *Which child is second? third? fourth?*

Display a cartoon or comic strip with speech balloons. Talk about how these are used to show what a character says. Draw a large speech balloon on the chalkboard and invite a volunteer to give you a quote about the weather. Write the child's words in the speech balloon. Then compare the quote in the speech balloon to one in a big book. Draw children's attention to the use of quotation marks to enclose the words that someone says.

Finally, talk about things that children do in winter. Have they ever made or seen a snowman? Ask: *What happens to snowmen when the sun comes out and the temperature rises?*

Introduce the Book

Display the model book that you made. Read it aloud and invite children to respond to the snowmen's stories. Ask: *Which one is worried about May? Why? In what season is May? Which snowman has some cheery news? What season is best for snowmen? Why?* As you read the story aloud the second time, have children listen for the number words. Ask them to name the number words they hear—*five, first, second, third, fourth, fifth.* Read the story once more and ask children to listen for the rhyming words. Ask them to name the

rhyming words they hear—*play, day; May, away; here, year.* On a subsequent reading, have children repeat the words that each snowman says. Explain that these words come after *said* in each sentence.

Make the Book

Duplicate and pass out pages 45–48 of this book. Have children assemble their *Five Frosty Snowmen* books and color the pictures. Draw attention to the speech balloons on pages 2–6. Ask children what words they think should go in the balloons. Have them copy the words of each snowman into the balloons. Or if students can work independently, let them write additional quotations that they make up for the snowmen to say in the balloons.

Share the Book

Call groups of five children to the front of the room. Assign each child to be a different snowman. Then read aloud the first line of the story and the first part ("The [first] one said...") of the other pages. Have the snowmen read aloud their own words.

Or chant the story aloud with the class. Challenge children to make up motions to go with the words.

Send the books home and encourage parents to respond on the comments page.

Beyond the Book

● Children might draw cartoons in which they use speech balloons.

● Teach the class other number rhymes, such as "Five Little Monkeys."

Teaching Tip: Use *Five Frosty Snowmen* to introduce children to quotation marks. Ask children if they can identify the quotation marks on the page and then talk about what quotation marks mean. Encourage them to find quotation marks in other printed material.

My Giant

SKILLS: Children make size comparisons.

Strategies for Starting

Establish some background with children by asking questions such as: *What is a giant? How big are giants? What giants have you read about or seen in a movie? What do you think giants like to do? Are they friendly? What do giants like to eat? How do they sound when they talk? Where do they live? Are giants always men?* Ask children if they would like to have a giant of their own. Have them describe how their giant would look and act. Invite children to show how a giant would walk and talk.

You might also consider reading a story such as "Jack and the Beanstalk" to the class at this time.

Introduce the Book

Display the model book that you made. Read it aloud to the class and point to the parts that you added. Ask children to start thinking about a giant of their own for the books they will make. Suggest that they have in mind a name, an idea of the giant's size, where the giant lives, what he eats, and some other activities that he likes to do.

Make the Book

Duplicate and pass out pages 49–53 of this book. Have children assemble their *My Giant* books. Then work with them to write and illustrate their stories. Children may need help spelling names or other words.

Share the Book

Have children take turns introducing their giants to the class by reading aloud their books and showing the pictures.

Send the books home for sharing and comments. When the books are returned to class with comments, use them as the centerpiece of a display on sizes.

Beyond the Book

● Create a mural of a giant and his kingdom.

● Write an owner's manual on how to care for a giant.

● Write a shopping list on how to feed a giant or write recipes on how to cook for a giant.

Bosco Shapes Up

SKILLS: Children use prepositions and prepositional phrases. Children focus on the benefits of exercise.

Strategies for Starting

Lead the class in a series of simple exercises such as touching toes, stretching arms over the head, and doing jumping jacks. Then generate a discussion of exercise as an important component of a healthy lifestyle. Develop an awareness and appreciation for the benefits of exercising.

Introduce the Book

Display the model copy you made of *Bosco Shapes Up*. Read the story to the class and share the illustrations. Discuss the ways Bosco exercises. Ask: *What is he doing on page 1? What happens to him on page 5? Is he acting silly on page 7? Do you*

think that Bosco has fun keeping in shape? Read the story again and emphasize the prepositions that you added to each page. Explain that the illustrations helped you decide what word to use. Point out that all the words you added are repeated on the last page of the book.

Make the Book

Duplicate and hand out pages 54–59 of this book. Have children assemble the books. Then have them complete the sentence on page 1 with the word *bear* and complete the sentences in the book with the correct prepositions. You may want to write the prepositions for the book on the chalkboard to help children choose the correct word to add to each page. Explain that for page 10, children should write the correct word next to each picture. Finally, have children color the illustrations.

Share the Book

Children might enjoy acting out the story of Bosco. Have members of a group take turns reading each page while a volunteer acts as Bosco. Designate appropriate props for Bosco's exercises beforehand.

Send the books home for children to read to or act out for family members.

Beyond the Book

As a class, brainstorm a list of different exercises and activities that the children like to do. Then create a class book by asking each children to write and illustrate one activity.

Teaching Tip: Practice using the prepositions in the book by positioning some object in relation to a desk or table. For example, place a book *under, on,* or *over* a table. Have children identify the prepositions. Introduce other prepositions that designate place. As children become comfortable with these words, have them take turns placing objects so the class can use prepositions to identify their positions.

When

SKILLS: Children focus on cause-and-effect relationships. Children work on social skills.

Strategies for Starting

Make up slips of paper with different scenarios such as: *You hurt your finger. You see a rainbow. You have to eat something that you don't like. You are on a ladder that is falling. You accidentally step on someone's foot. You meet someone you know. You receive a gift.* Place the papers in a pile facedown and have children take turns picking one and telling what they would say in response to the situation described. For example, they might say "Ouch!" if they hurt a finger or "Wow!" if they see a rainbow.

Introduce the Book

Display the sample book that you made and read it aloud to the class. Focus on the pattern, "I say ['hello'] when…" Invite children to think of other endings for each sentence. You may want to list some of these on a poster pad for children to refer to as they make their own books.

Make the Book

Duplicate and pass out pages 60–64 of this book. Have children assemble their *When* books. Then work with them to complete the statements. Have children illustrate the sentence on each page.

Share the Book

Children might read their books with partners. One student reads the first part of a statement (I say "Hello" when), and the partner reads his or her ending. Children can then change roles. Partners might conclude by writing comments on page 8 of each other's books.

Send the books home and invite parents to respond as well.

꩜ Beyond the Book

● Work on social skills with students. Develop appropriate responses for a variety of situations or circumstances. Talk about the importance of eye contact when speaking.

● Practice conversation with two or more students. Focus on the difference between hearing and listening. Develop an understanding of the importance of listening to, not just hearing someone.

● Work on the concepts of verbal and nonverbal communication. Talk about the importance of gestures and body language.

Teaching Tip: Give children practice reading people's facial expressions and gestures. Start by collecting a wide selection of pictures of people—magazines are a good source of photographs. Share the photos with children and ask them to talk about the mood of the person in the photograph.

My Book of Opposites

SKILLS: Children develop vocabulary by learning opposites.

꩜ Strategies for Starting

Play a game in which children pair up as opposites. Make up pairs of cards with opposites such as *hot/cold, in/out, dark/light, dirty/clean, slow/fast, loud/soft, win/lose, work/play, night/day, stop/go, full/empty, up/down, on/off, new/old, good/bad.*

Give one card to each child. Help children read the word on their cards. Then have children try to find their opposites. For example, a child with *in* must find a partner with *out*. When everyone is paired up, review all the opposites.

꩜ Introduce the Book

Show children the model book that you made. Read the book to the class, drawing attention to the pairs of opposites. Read the book again, this time having children supply the missing opposite to the second sentence on each page.

꩜ Make the Book

Duplicate and pass out pages 65–69 of this book. Have children assemble their *My Book of Opposites*. You might write the pairs of opposites that children will need on the chalkboard so that they can find and copy the appropriate words onto each page. Have children add illustrations to each page.

꩜ Share the Book

Children can team up with partners to read aloud their pairs of opposites.

Send the books home for children to share with their families.

꩜ Beyond the Book

● Create a list of additional opposites. Add to the list as children recognize or think of newly identified pairs of opposites.

● Work with students on understanding and identifying opposites. Develop illustrated lists.

● Have children work with partners to create their own books of opposites.

Big, Bigger

SKILLS: Children use comparative adjectives to describe size relationships.

◎ Strategies for Starting

Line up several children from shortest to tallest. Compare them to one another noting who is bigger or smaller. Have children say, "I am bigger than _____" or "I am smaller than _____." Point out that a person can be bigger than someone but smaller than someone else.

◎ Introduce the Book

Display the book that you made as a model. Draw children's attention to the title and cover illustration, then read the story. On a second reading, invite children to think of other items to compare. For example, ask: *What else is bigger than a pear? Smaller than a butterfly?* Point out and discuss the *-er* endings on words in the comparative form. Mention that children will be able to choose the objects that they compare on pages 3–9. On page 10, they will choose the attribute to compare.

◎ Make the Book

Duplicate and hand out copies of pages 70–75 of this book. After children assemble their books, work with them to think of comparisons for each page. Encourage children to use their imaginations. Have them illustrate each comparison.

◎ Share the Book

Invite volunteers to read aloud their comparisons and to share the illustrations that go with them.

Have children take the books home to read with their families. When the books are returned to class with comments, place them in a math corner.

◎ Beyond the Book

Broaden the scope of the lesson to include superlatives and their use. Make books or other items in three sizes—big, bigger, biggest.

One Bright Monday Morning

SKILLS: Children relate text with a counting format to corresponding pictures. Children focus on verb forms with *-ing*. Children identify signs of spring.

◎ Strategies for Starting

Have students think about some of the things that they might observe on a spring walk in their neighborhoods. Ask: *What are people and animals doing when you see them? What are plants doing? Insects? Cars and trucks?* Have children express their responses as *-ing* words. For example, "I see boys skating."

Have children act out *-ing* words *(running, yawning, frowning, laughing, itching, jumping, crawling, washing)* that you whisper to them. Can their classmates guess what they are doing?

◎ Introduce the Book

Read aloud the sample book that you made. Emphasize the *-ing* words. Have children count the animals, plants, or people in the pictures to verify that the numbers correspond to the text.

🌀 Make the Book

Duplicate and pass out copies of pages 76–83 of this book. After children assemble the pages and color the pictures, have them cut apart the text on page 83. Explain that they are to glue the appropriate text to each book page. Review the text with the class before children begin gluing.

🌀 Share the Book

Children might do a choral reading of their books for another class. Have them practice saying the *-ing* words with different expressions.

Send the books home for children to share with their families. When the books are returned to class with comments, include them in a science corner or on a bulletin board display with a seasonal theme.

🌀 Beyond the Book

● Enjoy similar selections such as "There Was an Old Lady Who Swallowed a Fly" or "This Is the House That Jack Built."

● Study weather words and watch for signs of spring.

The Farm

SKILLS: Children focus on farm animals and learn how pictures can support text.

🌀 Strategies for Starting

Display pictures of farms and farm animals. Invite children to share their experiences or knowledge of farms. Discuss the sounds that various animals make. Ask: *Where on a farm would you find a horse? a pig? a cat?*

🌀 Introduce the Book

Show children the sample book that you made. Read aloud the first two pages. Then invite children to follow the pattern and join in after you read the first line of each of the verses. Repeat until children are familiar with the pattern. Does the ending surprise them?

Draw children's attention to the phrase "in the [barn]." Can they find it in each verse? Which words in each verse tell what the animal says? Point out that in this book children will use clues from the text to draw a background around the animal and write what the animal says in the speech balloon. For example, they should draw a barn around the cow and write "Moo" in the speech balloon.

🌀 Make the Book

Duplicate pages 84–89 of this book. Have children assemble their *The Farm* books. Set aside time for them to complete the illustrations and write in the speech balloons.

🌀 Share the Book

Children might read their books to another class. Suggest that they invite their audience to join in when the animals "speak."

Have children take their books home for families to read and respond to.

🌀 Beyond the Book

● Make labels for the classroom using *in the... (in the basket, in the bottle, in the desk, in the closet, in the trash, in the drawer, in the box, in the cabinet).*

● Using the literary pattern in the selection, develop new verses. Illustrate the poems to provide picture clues for the text. Make a class book of the new poems. This is an excellent vehicle for emergent readers to make the connection between print and word meaning. The picture clues and patterned responses facilitate one-to-one match and word correspondence.

How to Make a Scarecrow

SKILLS: Children order events and recognize sequence words.

Strategies for Starting

Discuss the purposes of scarecrows. Ask: *Where do you find them? What is the purpose of a scarecrow in the spring? What is the purpose of a scarecrow in autumn?*

If possible, show children illustrations or photographs of scarecrows.

Introduce the Book

Display the book that you made as a model. Draw children's attention to the title. Explain that to make this book, you had to put the steps for making a scarecrow in order and that you used sequence words as clues. On the chalkboard, write the words *first, next, then, finally.* Discuss how these words helped you decide on the correct sequence and how you were able to confirm your ideas about the sequence by looking at the illustrations.

Make the Book

Duplicate and pass out pages 90–93 of this book. Have children assemble the books and cut apart the text on page 93. Suggest that children put the text in order before they begin to paste it on the pages of the book. When the text is in place, have children color the illustrations.

Share the Book

Consider having children make a large paper scarecrow following the steps in their books.

Send the books home for sharing and family responses.

Beyond the Book

● Work with students on the parts of a story dealing with beginning, middle, and end. Consider words and phrases that might signal these parts such as *once upon a time, first, second, next, then, finally, at last.* Practice telling a story that includes some of these sequence words. When retelling a story, omit a part of the story such as the beginning or end and have students identify and put in the missing part.

● Using a similar literary pattern, develop a story or book about how to make a sandwich, how to make a jack-o'lantern, or how to make a snowman.

● Extend the discussions of scarecrows to broader background information on gardens by describing the sequential steps in planting and caring for plants.

Send-Home Reproducible

Explain the educational purpose of write-and-read books and encourage family members to read and respond to their children's work by sending home the letter on the following page.

_____
Fecha

Queridos familiares,

Como parte del programa de enseñanza de la lectura, nuestra clase está haciendo una serie de libros llamada "Escribe y Lee".

Las historias en esos libros siguen el simple patrón que usamos para leer en clase. Los niños están muy orgullosos de estos libros y quieren compartirlos con ustedes. Por eso, les pedimos que por favor traten de encontrar un momento para leer y hablar juntos sobre ellos.

En la contratapa de cada libro encontrarán una página que dice: "Comentarios". Para su niño será muy importante que escriban uno o dos comentarios positivos sobre el libro o sobre la forma en que el niño lo lee. Por ejemplo, pueden comentar sobre la historia, las ideas, las ilustraciones, la escritura o la presentación en general u opinar sobre la forma en que su niño lee y si lo hace de corrido y con expresión. También pueden hacer notar cómo explica las palabras difíciles y si usa los indicios del contexto, además del aumento de su vocabulario y otras mejoras en general.

Por favor devuelvan los libros a la escuela con sus comentarios antes del

_____

Le agradecemos desde ya su participación. Su interés y apoyo significará mucho para su pequeño lector.

Sinceramente,

_____

2

Veo un

_____

anaranjado. ¿Lo ves tú?

1

Veo una

_____

roja. ¿La ves tú?

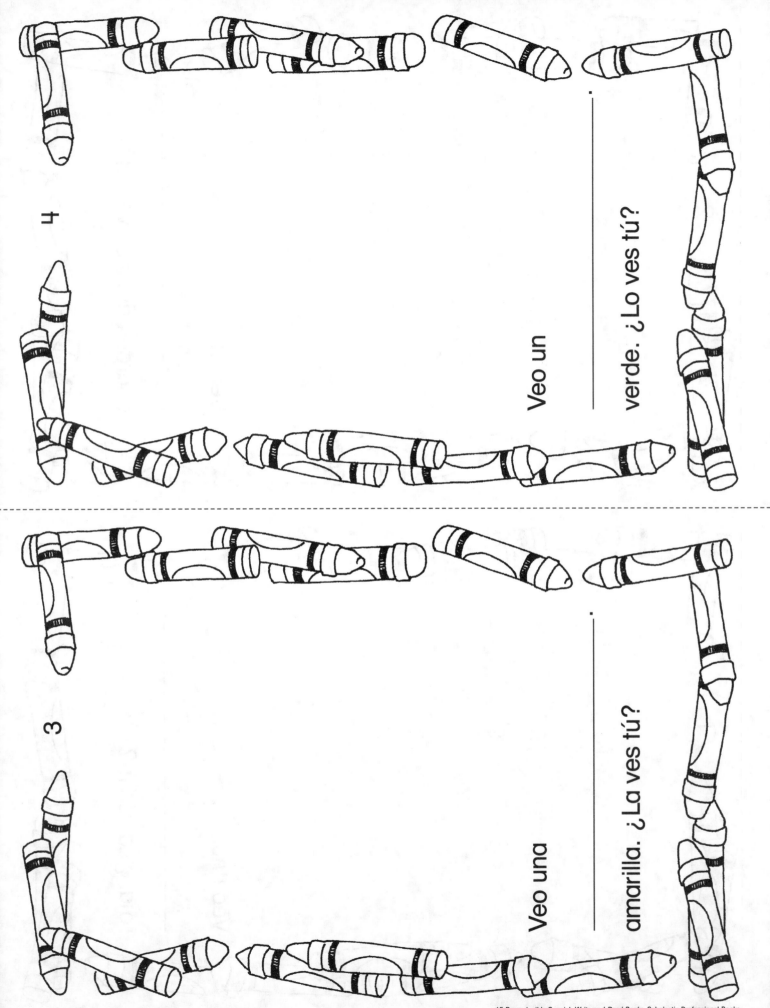

4

Veo un _____ verde. ¿Lo ves tú?

3

Veo una _____ amarilla. ¿La ves tú?

¿Qué me pongo?

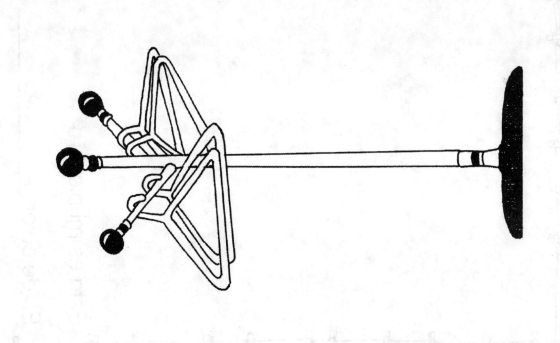

por _____

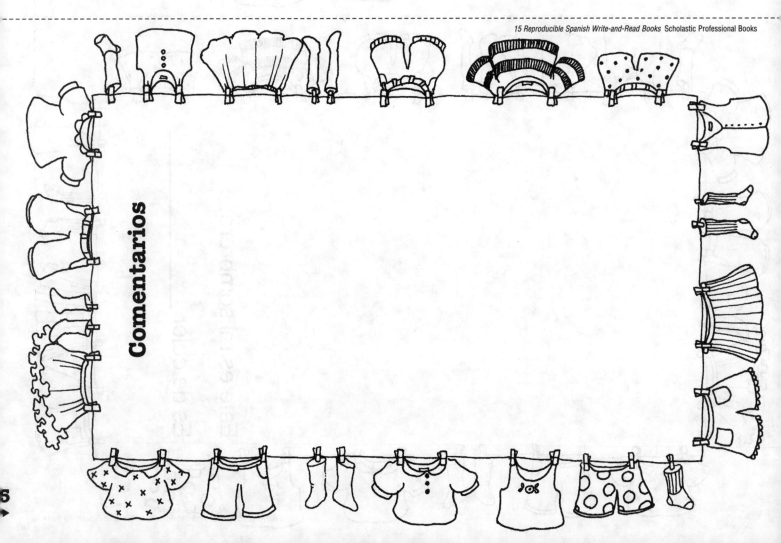

Comentarios

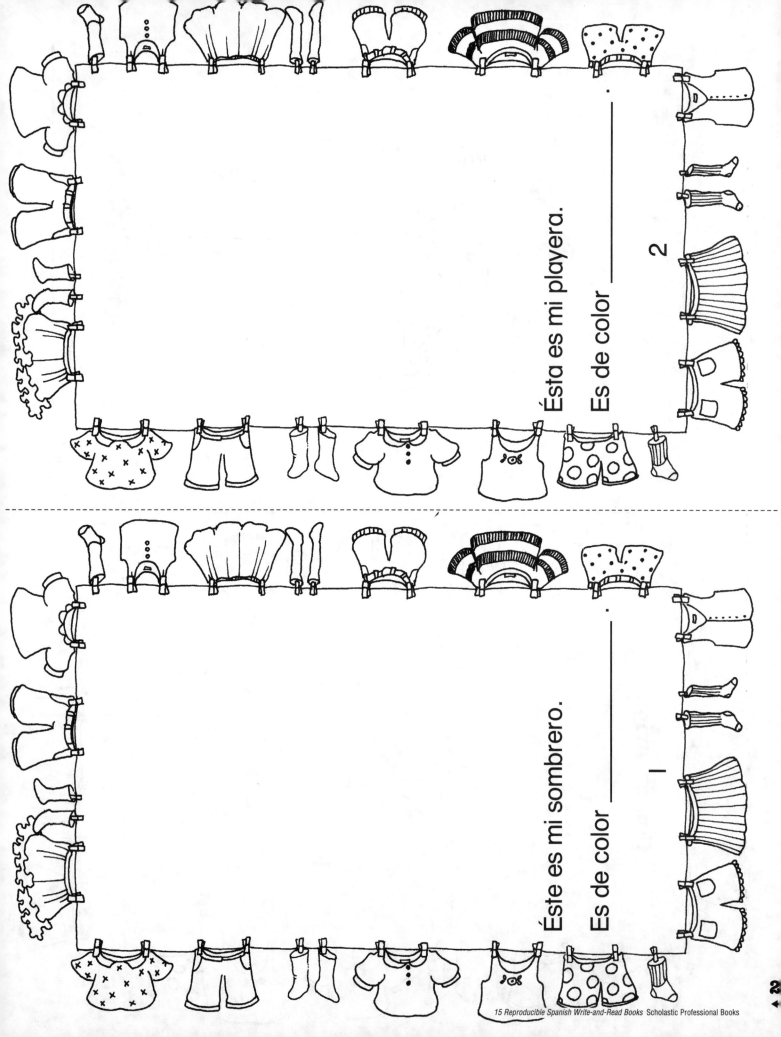

Ésta es mi playera.

Es de color _____ .

2

Éste es mi sombrero.

Es de color _____ .

1

Éstos son mis calcetines.

Son de color _____.

4

Éstos son mis pantalones.

Son de color _____.

3

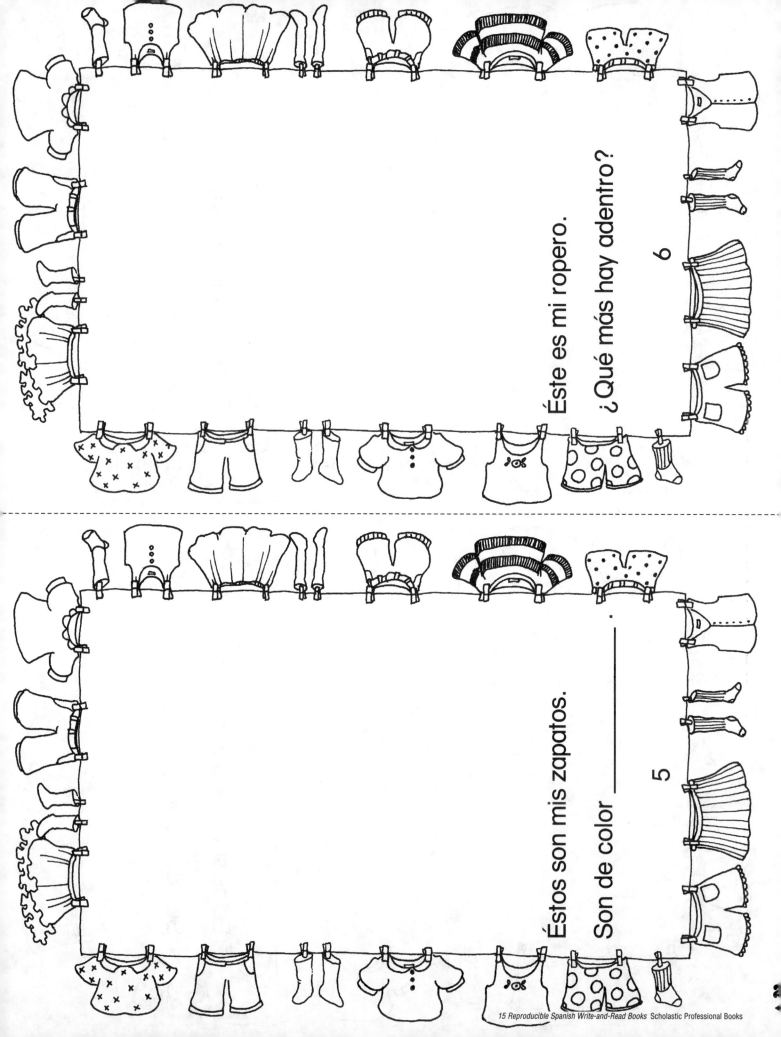

Éste es mi ropero.

¿Qué más hay adentro?

6

Éstos son mis zapatos.

Son de color _____ .

5

Mi amigo

por _____

15 Reproducible Spanish Write-and-Read Books Scholastic Professional Books

Comentarios

Siempre _____

juntos.

2

_____ es mi amigo.

1

15 Reproducible Spanish Write-and-Read Books Scholastic Professional Books

Cuando llueve jugamos

_____ adentro.

4

Cuando hay sol jugamos

_____ afuera.

3

15 Reproducible Spanish Write-and-Read Books Scholastic Professional Books

Lo que más me gusta de mi amigo

es _____.

6

Otro juego que jugamos

juntos es _____.

5

Lo mejor de mi mascota es

_____

4

Mi mascota duerme

_____

3

15 Reproducible Spanish Write-and-Read Books Scholastic Professional Books

¿Usan los cerdos peluca?

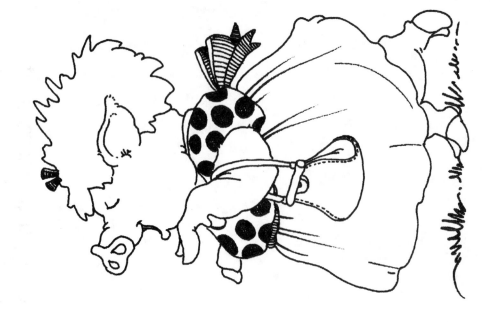

por _____

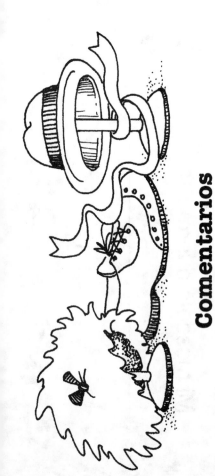

Comentarios

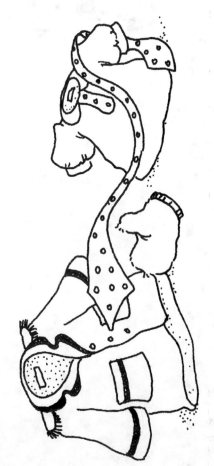

3

¿ Usan los canguros _____?

2

¿ Usan los cerdos _____?

1

¿Usan los gatitos _____?

4

¿Usan las cabras _____?

3

38

¿Usan los monitos

6

¿Usan los ratoncitos

5

15 Reproducible Spanish Write-and-Read Books Scholastic Professional Books

¿Usan las ratitas _____?

8

¿Usan las moscas _____?

7

15 Reproducible Write-and-Read Books Scholastic Professional Books

¡Qué sorpresa!

por _____

Comentarios

1

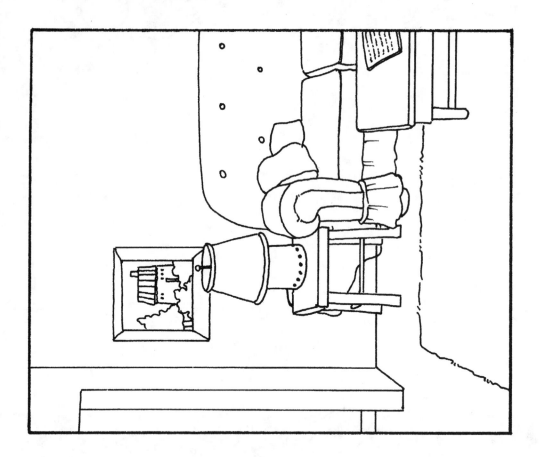

Entré a la _____.

No había nadie.

2

Entré al pasillo.

No había nadie.

1

4

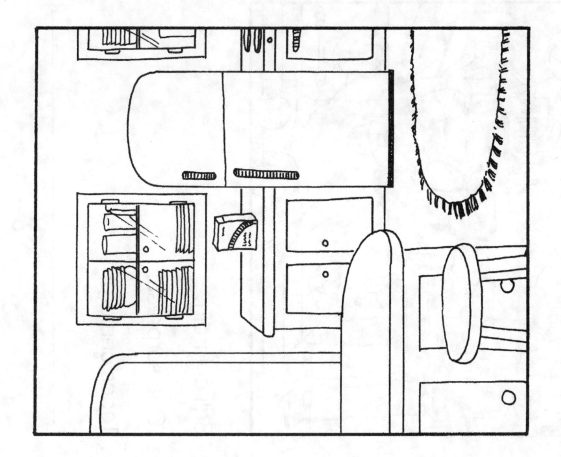

Entré a la _____.

4

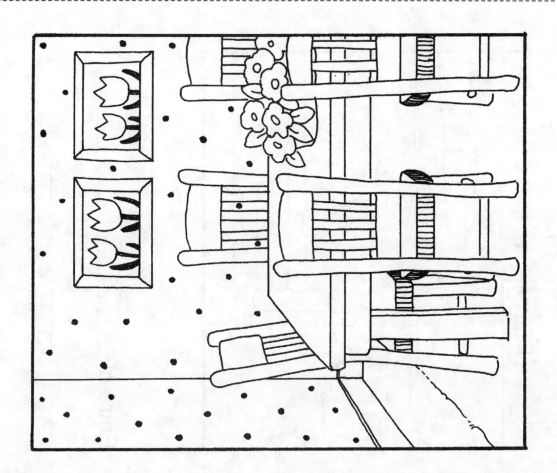

Entré al _____.

No había nadie.

3

Salí al jardín.

¡Qué sorpresa!

¡Todos cantaron

6

Entré al _____.

5

Cinco muñecos de nieve

por _____

Comentarios

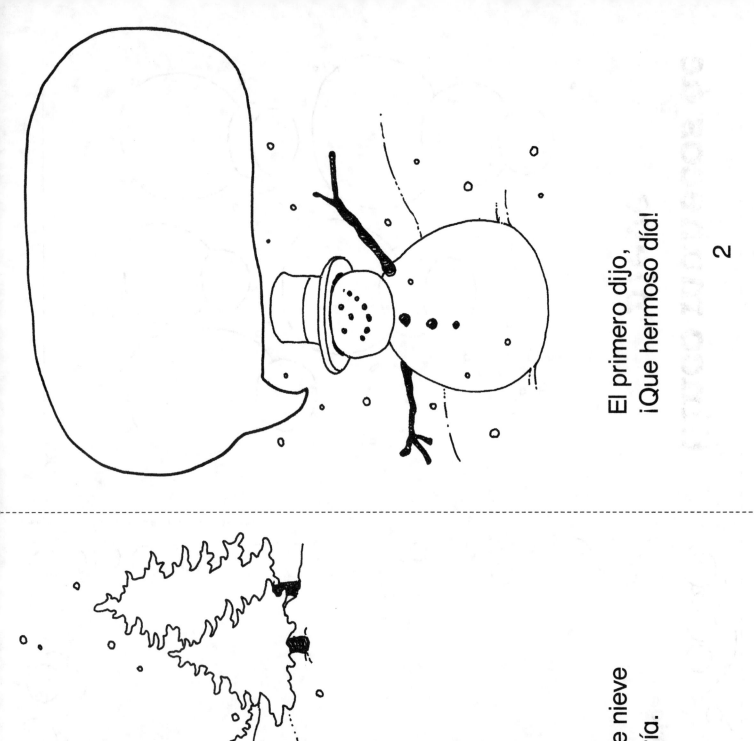

El primero dijo,
¡Que hermoso día!

2

Cinco muñecos de nieve
jugaban con alegría.

1

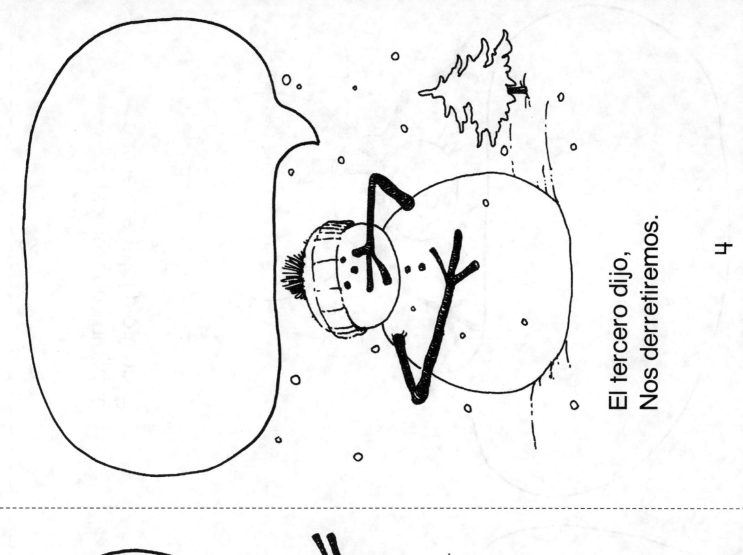

El tercero dijo,
Nos derretiremos.

4

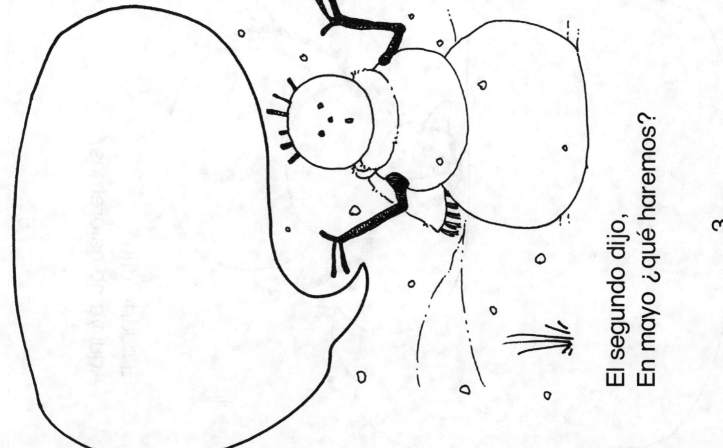

El segundo dijo,
En mayo ¿qué haremos?

3

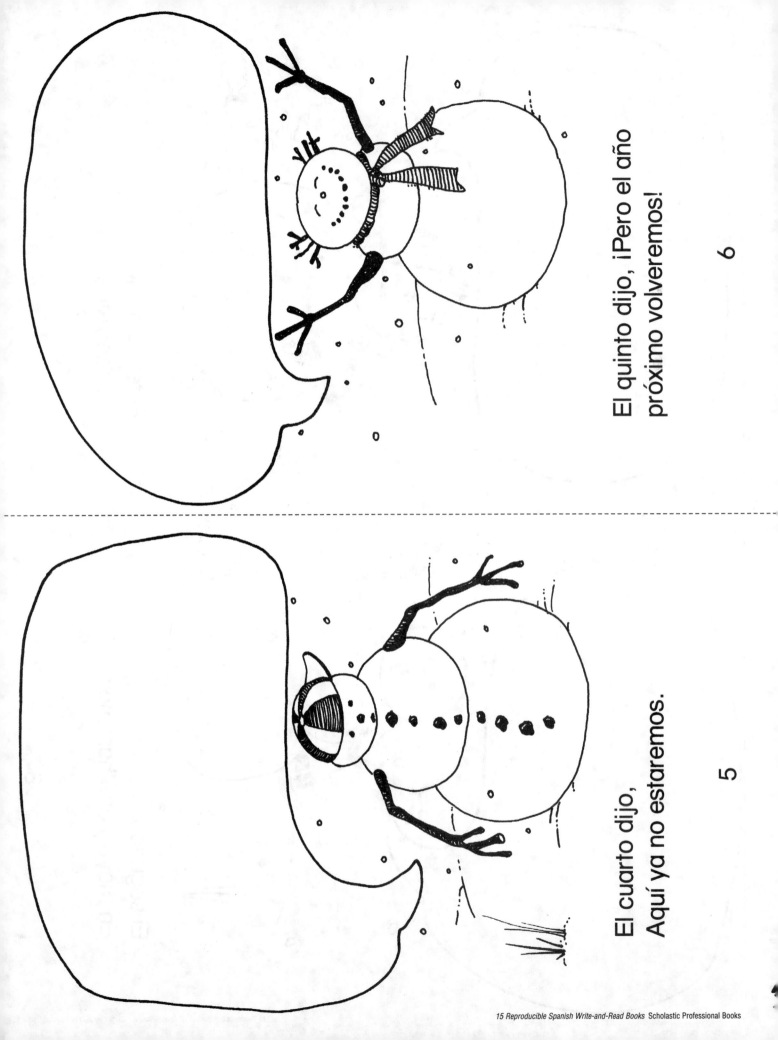

El quinto dijo, ¡Pero el año
próximo volveremos!

6

El cuarto dijo,
Aquí ya no estaremos.

5

Mi gigante

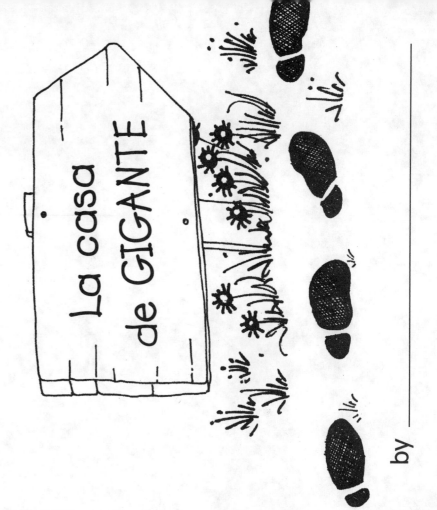

La casa de GIGANTE

by _____

15 Reproducible Spanish Write-and-Read Books Scholastic Professional Books

Comentarios

Mi gigante es más grande que

_____

2

Esté es mi gigante.

Se llama _____

1

GIGANTE

Aquí es donde vive mi gigante.

Es _____ .

4

Pero no tan grande como _____ .

3

A mi gigante le gusta

6

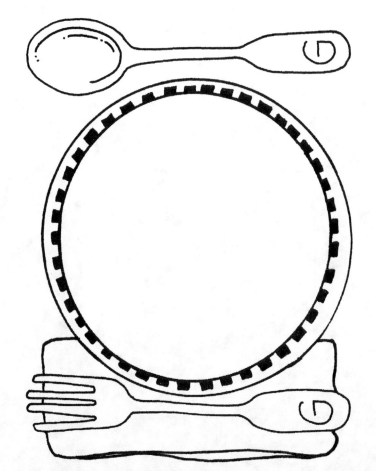

Ésta es su cena.

Él come _____

5

Mi gigante y yo

8

A mi gigante le gusta

7

Bosco hace ejercicios

por _____

15 Reproducible Spanish Write-and-Read Books Scholastic Professional Books

Comentarios

Bosco _____ las escaleras.

2

Bosco es un _____.

Le gusta hacer ejercicios.

1

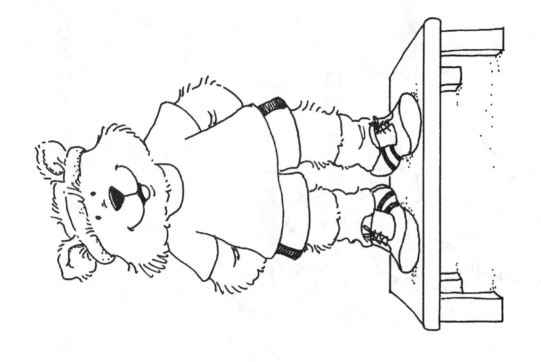

Bosco ésta _____

del banco.

4

Bosco _____ las escaleras.

3

Bosco salta _____ el colchón.

6

Bosco ésta _____
del banco.

5

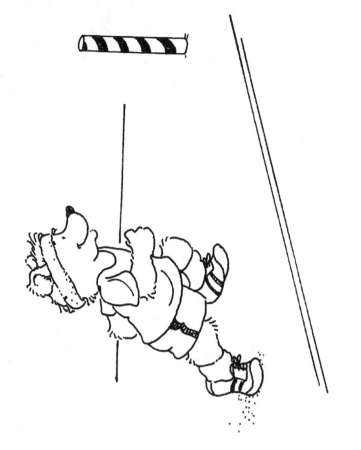

Bosco corre _____ el poste.

8

Bosco se esconde _____

del colchón.

7

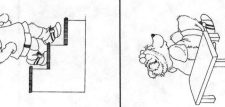
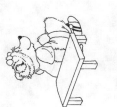

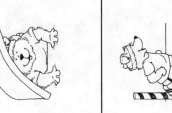

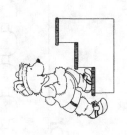

Bosco hace ejercicios todos los días.

10

Bosco corre _____ el poste.

9

15 Reproducible Spanish Write-and-Read Books Scholastic Professional Books

Cuando

por _____

Comentarios

Digo "Adiós" cuando

_____

_____.

2

Digo "Hola" cuando

_____

_____.

1

Digo "Auxilio" cuando

_____

_____ .

4

Digo "Disculpe" cuando

_____

_____ .

3

Digo "Por favor" cuando

_____

_____ .

6

Digo "Gracias" cuando

_____

_____ .

5

Digo "Buenas Noches" cuando

_____

_____ .

8

Digo "Oh, no" cuando

_____

_____

7

Mi libro de los opuestos

por _____

Comentarios

Cuando mi equipo gana, nosotros _____.

L L E G A D A

Cuando mi equipo pierde, nosotros _____.

2

En el verano tengo _____.

En el invierno tengo _____.

1

Cuando sale la luna, es _____.

4

Cuando sale el sol, es _____.

Cuando susurro, mi voz es _____.

3

Cuando grito, mi voz es _____.

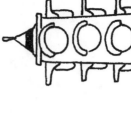

Cuando se prende la luz roja,

los autos deben

Cuando se prende la luz verde,

los autos pueden

6

Cuando voy a la escuela, yo

Cuando estoy en casa, yo

5

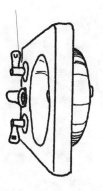

Antes de lavarme, estoy

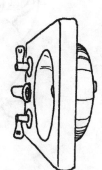

Después de lavarme, estoy

8

Cuando pongo leche, mi vaso está

Cuando tomo la leche, mi vaso está

7

Grande, más grande

por _____

Comentarios

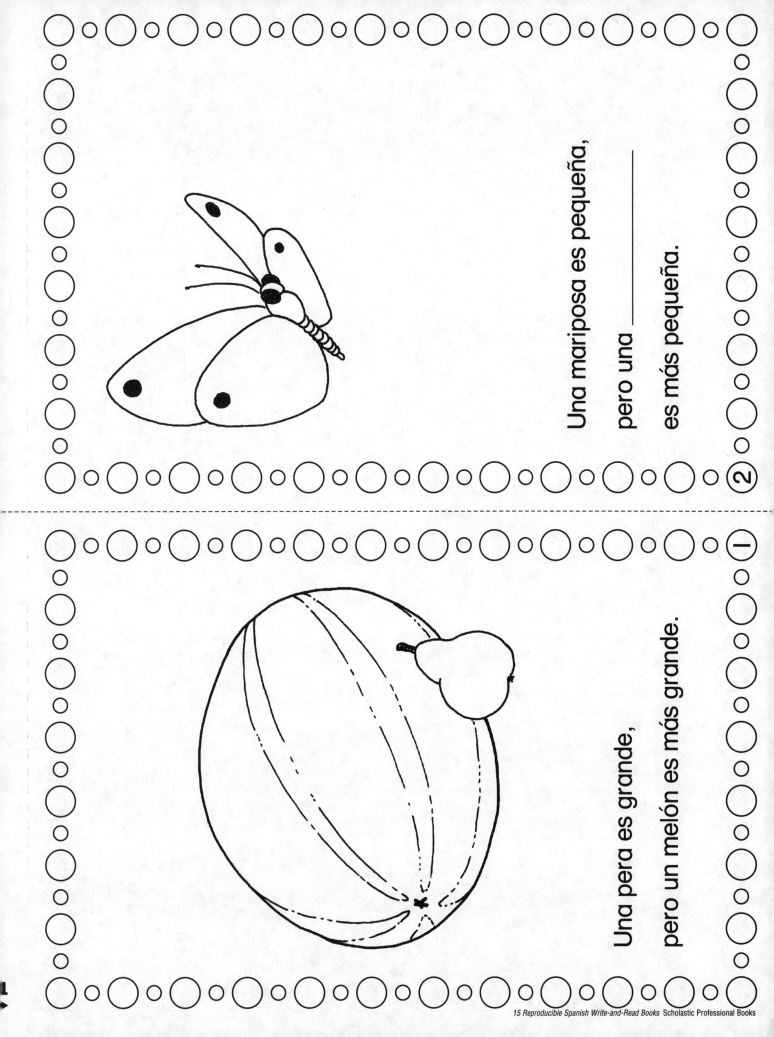

Una mariposa es pequeña,

pero una _____

es más pequeña.

②

Una pera es grande,

pero un melón es más grande.

①

Una _____ es corta,

pero una _____

es más corta.

4

Un _____ es largo,

pero un _____

es más largo.

3

Un _____

pero un _____ es gordo,

es más gordo.

⑥

_____ es alto,

Un _____

pero un _____

es más alto.

⑤

3

Una _____ es rápida,

pero una _____

es más rápida.

⑧

Una _____ es flaca,

pero una _____

es más flaca.

⑦

Yo soy _____,

pero _____

es _____.

10

Una _____ es lenta,

pero una _____

es más lenta.

9

Una mañana de sol

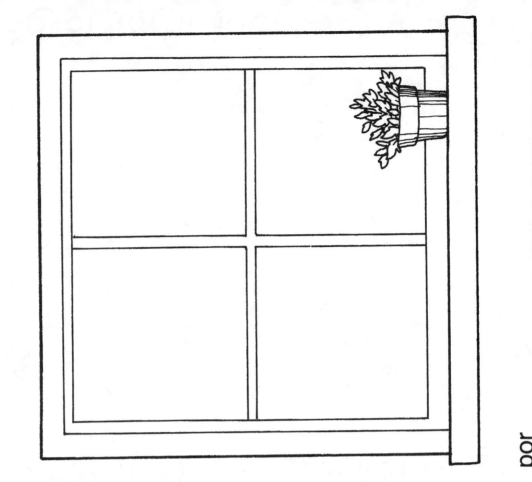

por _____

15 Reproducible Spanish Write-and-Read Books Scholastic Professional Books

comentarios

2

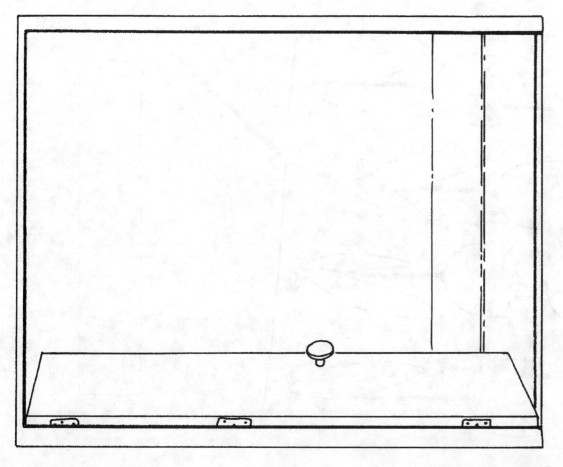

Una mañana de sol, salí a
caminar y vi . . . .

1

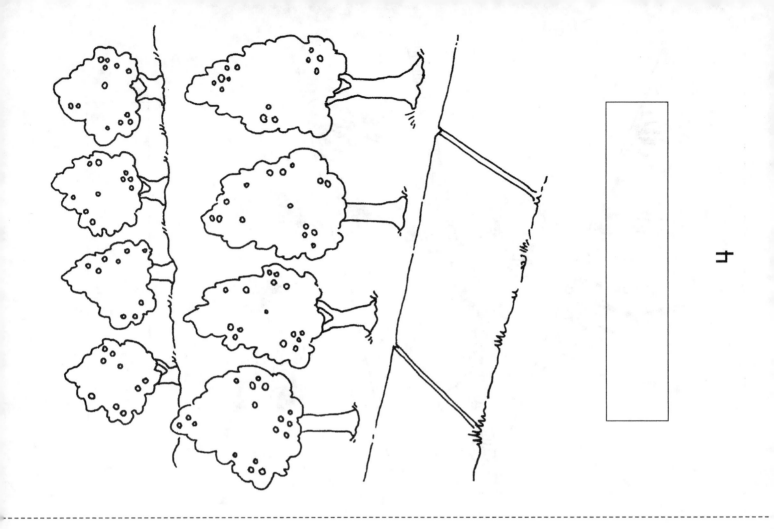

4

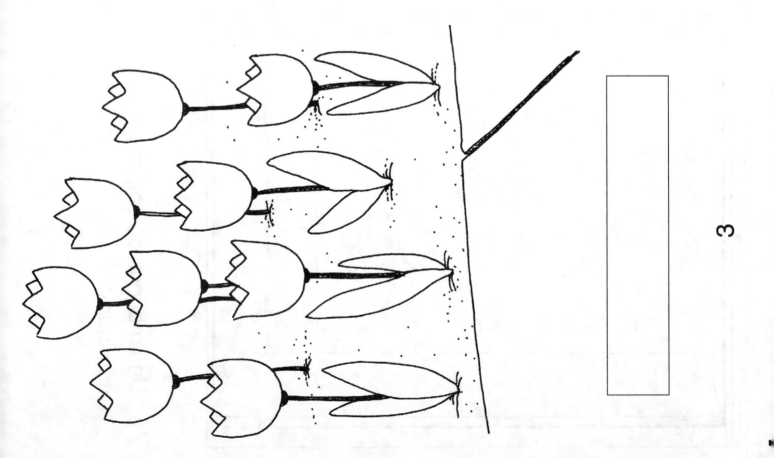

3

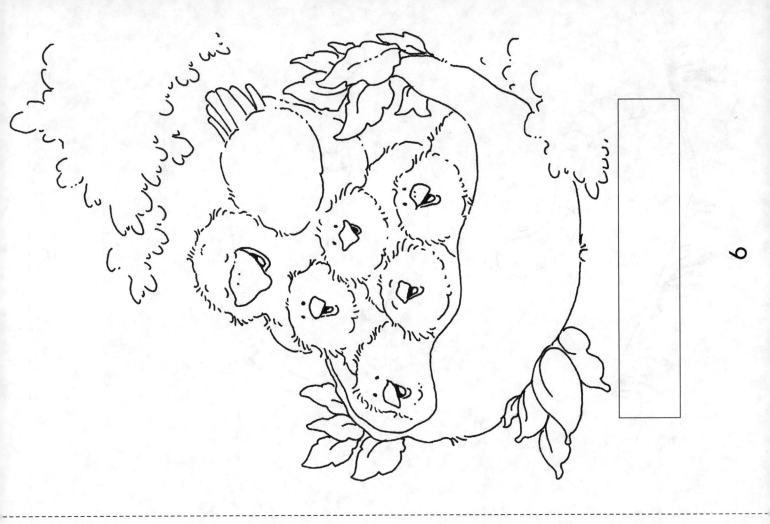

6

5

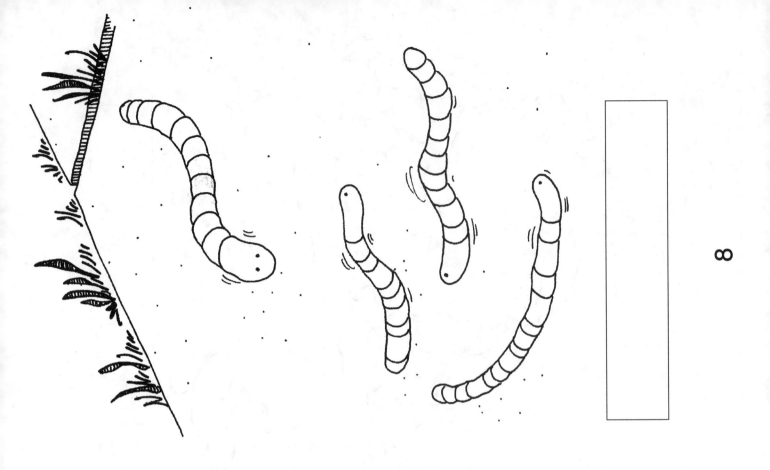

8

7

10

9

12

FIESTA DE LA PRIMAVERA

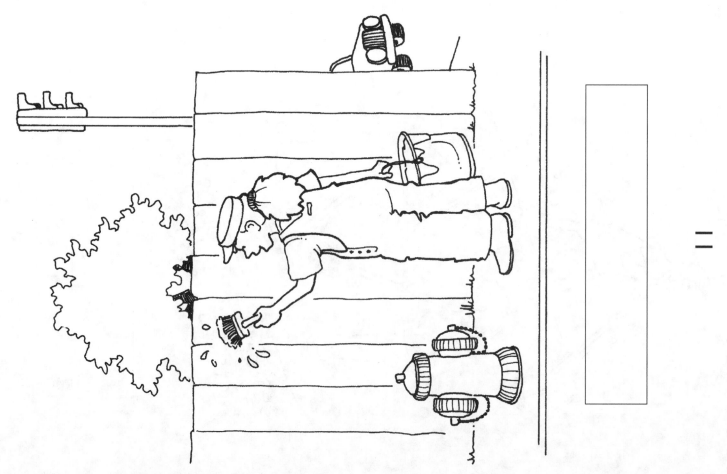

11

10 hormiguitas caminando,

9 flores brotando,

8 cerezos floreciendo,

7 payasos saltando,

6 pájaros cantando,

5 abejas volando,

4 lombrices meneándose,

3 personas limpiando,

2 cometas volando,

y una pintora pintando.

La granja

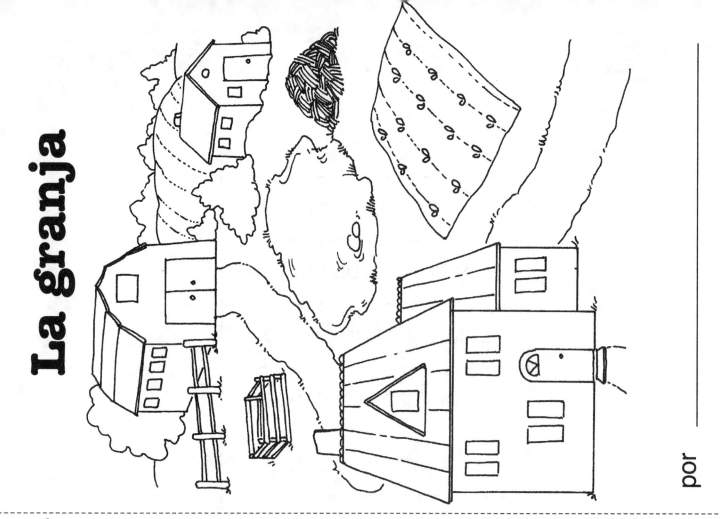

por _____

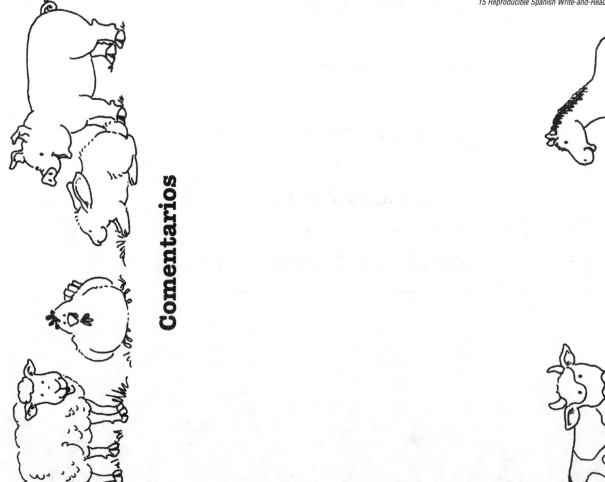

Comentarios

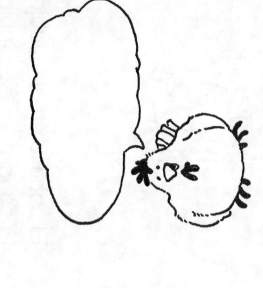

La gallina en el gallinero,
La gallina en el gallinero.
Clo, clo,
Clo, clo.
La gallina en el gallinero.

2

La vaca en el corral,
La vaca en el corral.
Muuu, muuu,
Muuu, muuu.
La vaca en el corral..

1

El caballo en el establo,
El caballo en el establo.
Hin, hin,
Hin, hin.
El caballo en el establo.

4

El pato en la laguna,
El pato en la laguna.
Cuac, cuac,
Cuac, cuac.
El pato en la laguna.

3

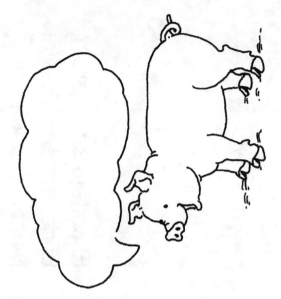

El cerdo en la pocilga,
El cerdo en la pocilga.
Oink, oink,
Oink, oink.
El cerdo en la pocilga.

6

El perro en el patio,
El perro en el patio.
Guau, guau,
Guau, guau.
El perro en el patio.

5

El conejo en el jardín,
El conejo en el jardín.
Munch, munch,
Munch, munch.
El conejo en el jardín.

8

La oveja en el prado,
La oveja en el prado.
Bee, bee,
Bee, bee.
La oveja en el prado.

7

Los niños en el pajar,
Los niños en el pajar.
¡Hurra! ¡Hurra!
¡Hurra! ¡Hurra!
Los niños en el pajar.

10

El gato en la canasta,
El gato en la canasta.
Miau, miau,
Miau, miau.
El gato en la canasta.

9

Para hacer un espantapájaros

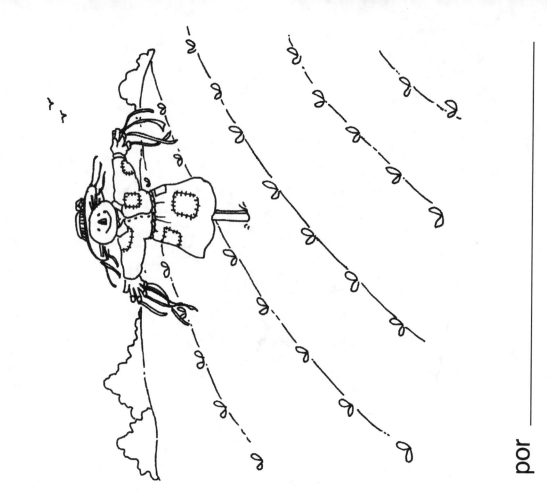

por _____

Comentarios

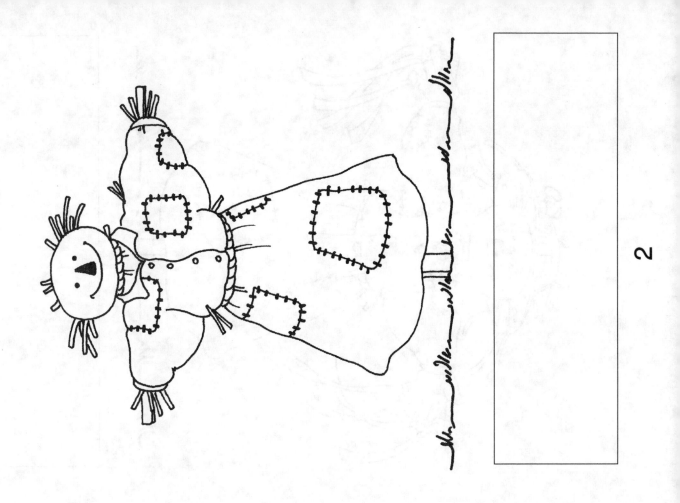

2

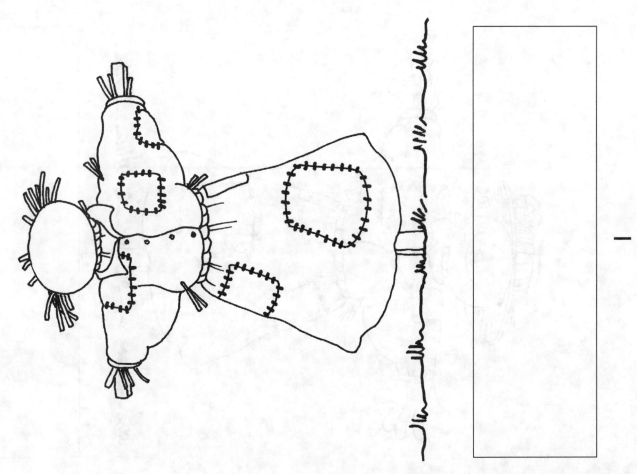

1

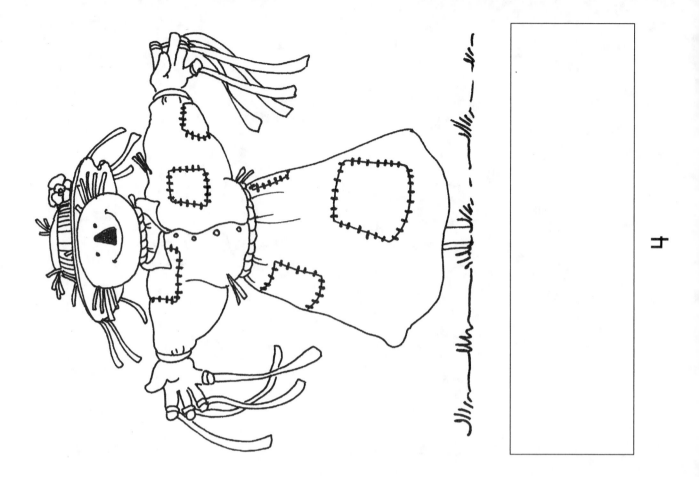

4

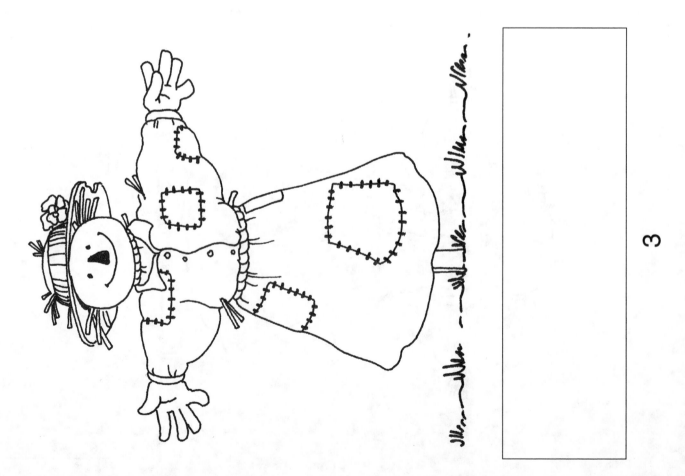

3

Hemos hecho un espantapájaros.
Se hace así.
Primero le pusimos una falda y
una camisa vieja.

Luego, le pintamos una cara.

Luego, le pusimos un sombrero.
Y también un par de guantes.

Para terminar, le atamos unos
pedazos de tela en los dos dedos.

Esta es la foto de _____ .

Sobre el autor

Este libro fue hecho por _____ .

_____ tiene _____ años de

edad. A _____ le gusta

_____ , _____ , y

_____ .

Otros libros por este autor son

_____

_____

_____

_____

por

Comentarios